nickelodeon™

Winx CLUB™

Annual 2014

EGMONT
We bring stories to life

First published in Great Britain 2013
by Egmont UK Limited, 1st Floor, The Yellow Building,
1 Nicholas Road, London W11 4AN

Activities and story adaptations by Catherine Shoolbred.
Designed by Anthony Duke.

Stories based on Special 2: Revenge of the Trix, Special 3: Winx Club: The Battle for Magix,
Special 4: The Shadow Phoenix, Episode 501: The Spill and Episode 502: The Rise of Tritannus.

ISBN 978 1 4052 6764 9
54730/1
Printed in Italy

Stay safe online. Any website addresses listed in this book are correct at the time of going to print. However, Egmont is not
responsible for content hosted by third parties. Please be aware that online content can be subject to change and websites
can contain content that is unsuitable for children. We advise that all children are supervised when using the internet.

Adult supervision is recommended for all craft and cookery activities featured.

What's Inside ...

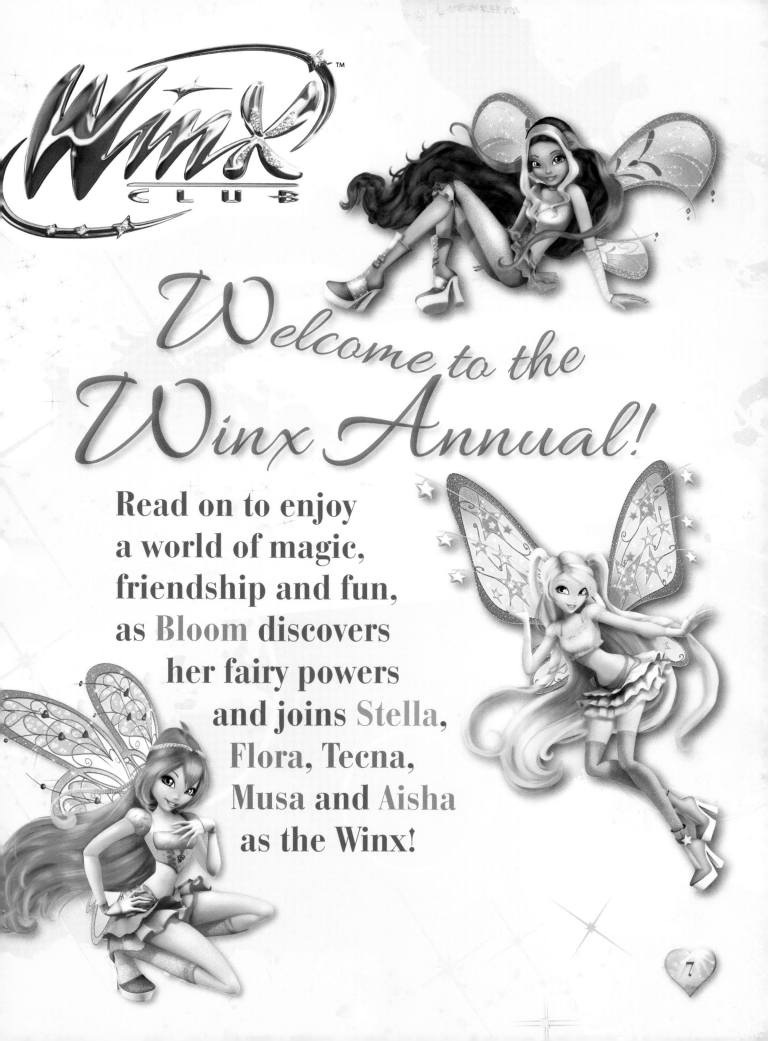

Welcome to the Winx Annual!

Read on to enjoy
a world of magic,
friendship and fun,
as **Bloom** discovers
her fairy powers
and joins **Stella**,
Flora, **Tecna**,
Musa and **Aisha**
as the Winx!

All About Bloom ...

FAIRY POWER: Fairy of the Dragon Flame

LIKES: Leading the Winx Club and learning new spells.

LOVES: Her true love, Prince Sky, and Kiko, her pet rabbit.

STRENGTHS: Loyal friend and an awesome fighter who never gives up!

FAVOURITE SPELL: Dragon's Flame

FAMILY: Bloom was adopted as a baby by her human parents, Vanessa and Mike. She later discovers she's a fairy and a princess of the planet Domino! Her real parents are Queen Marion and King Oritel and she has a sister called Daphne.

HOME: Gardenia on Earth, although Bloom was born on the planet Domino in the Magic Dimension.

PIXIE FRIEND: Lockette, the Pixie of Direction. Lockette helps Bloom find her way physically and emotionally, as she discovers the truth about her past.

MAGIC PETS: Kiko the Rabbit and Belle the Sheep.

Bloom's amazed to discover that Kiko is magical too! Draw a tasty carrot for him to eat.

KIKO

9

Bloom's Dreams

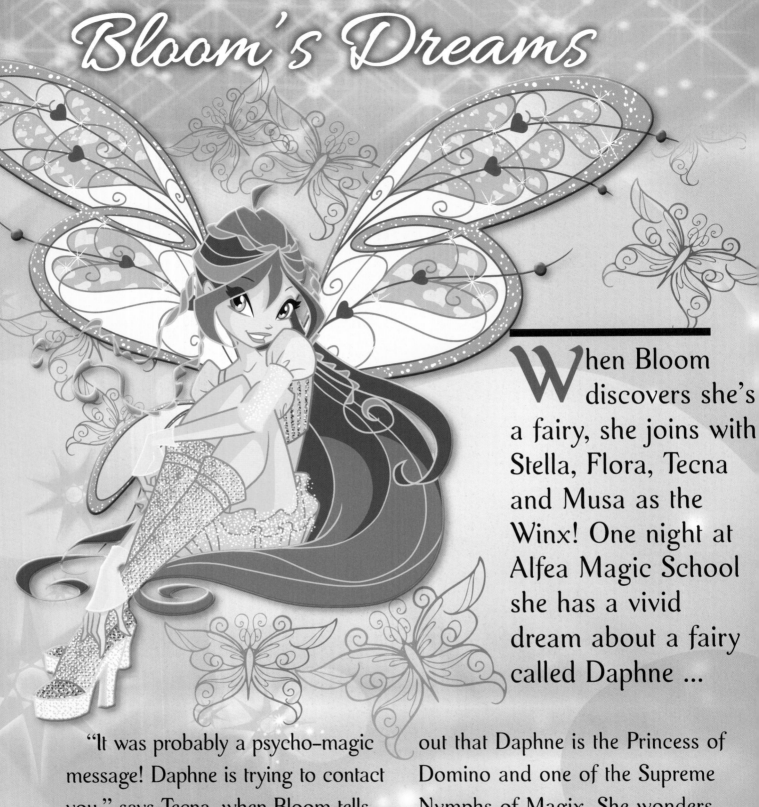

When Bloom discovers she's a fairy, she joins with Stella, Flora, Tecna and Musa as the Winx! One night at Alfea Magic School she has a vivid dream about a fairy called Daphne ...

"It was probably a psycho–magic message! Daphne is trying to contact you," says Tecna, when Bloom tells the Winx about her dream.

In the magic library, Bloom finds out that Daphne is the Princess of Domino and one of the Supreme Nymphs of Magix. She wonders why she's dreaming about her.

Meanwhile, the evil Trix witches

persuade Riven, a Specialist boy wizard, to work with them.

"We can make you powerful if you tell us all about the Winx," Darcy smirks, as he agrees.

When Bloom visits her family, she has another vivid dream. She's a baby again and her firefighter father rescues her from a burning building. Mike explains that the dream was a memory.

"The whole place was on fire but the flames protected you. We always planned to tell you, but all of a sudden it was too late," he adds, as he explains that he and Vanessa went on to adopt her.

"We loved you from the first moment and we'll never stop," her mother adds.

"I love you both too," Bloom smiles, as she hugs them.

When Bloom returns to Alfea, the headmistress, Miss Faragonda, sends her into a magical vision to see everything she knows about Daphne. In the vision, Daphne shows Bloom a crown.

"I hope that's enough, you must end your search now, " Miss Faragonda tells her. "There are powerful forces at work here."

At Cloudtower, the school of witches, Mirta overhears the Trix, Icy, Darcy and Stormy, planning to trick Bloom into thinking she's a witch so they can take her powers. Mirta decides to warn Bloom.

Since discovering that she was adopted, Bloom has wondered who her birth family

were. Prince Sky agrees to helps her break into Cloudtower's Archive to find the magic book that will answer any question, so Bloom can ask it about her past. Riven tells the Trix what she's doing, so they put their evil plan into action.

So when Bloom asks the magic book who she really is, the three Ancestral Witches say: "You are a witch like us!" Sky steps away in surprise and shocked Bloom runs away.

The next day, everyone looks for Bloom. Mirta finds her first, and tells her about the Trix's trick. She and Bloom are captured by Icy, but the Winx come to their rescue. Soon, the witches and fairies are battling fiercely.

"Stop it!" Mirta yells at the Trix, as she conjures up an angry monster which blasts them away.

Furious, Icy turns Mirta into a pumpkin. But as she does, Bloom calls up her inner dragon, which zaps into the sky, making the Trix disappear. The fairies take pumpkin Mirta back to Alfea with them.

Bloom is pleased that she's not a witch, but she's worried that she hasn't heard from Sky. She asks him to meet her at the Dragon Exhibition the next day, but he tells her that it's only for VIPs, so she can't go.

Prince Sky tells his friend Timmy why he has been avoiding Bloom. "I'm supposed to marry Princess Diaspro, but I love Bloom!" he tells him sadly.

The Winx help Bloom sneak into the Dragon Exhibition to find Prince Sky. But she's heartbroken

to see him with Diaspro. Tearfully, she packs her bags and goes home to Gardenia. But when she arrives, she finds the Trix have captured her parents!

"What do you want!" Bloom cries in horror.

"The Dragon Flame!" Icy replies. "Years ago our Ancestor witches found the greatest power in the Magic Dimension was in you, Bloom. But your meddling sister Daphne hid you in Gardenia, so the Ancients got rid of her and destroyed your home planet Domino."

"And now we're taking your Dragon Flame," Stormy laughs.

Bloom is amazed to hear that Daphne is her sister and she's horrified to hear what happened to her and to Domino. Bloom tries to fight off the Trix, but they rip out her powers and fly away gleefully. What will become of Bloom now?

See what happens next on

PAGE 20 ...

Dream On!

The Winx love telling each other their dreams.
Read on to discover what your dreams might mean too!

Failing a Test

These dreams usually
mean you feel tested
in some way
and feel unprepared.

Being Chased

This could mean you're stressed
about school or about an
argument with a friend. Sort out
what's bugging you and you'll
chase this dream away.

Flying

These are awesome dreams,
which make you feel powerful.
You must be feeling really good
to dream about flying.

Getting Lost
or Trapped

These dreams can mean you
have a problem in real life and
need to find a solution to it.

Falling

You may have this dream if
you did badly in a test or were
embarrassed in public. Have fun
with friends and you'll soon
feel good again.

Cat
Watch your enemies

Horse
A sign of happiness

Happy Dog
Brings many friends

Animal Dreams
Some people believe dreaming about animals can predict the future!

Barking Dog
Brings bad news

Rat
Trouble ahead

Eagle
Fame and wealth

Why do we dream?

No one really knows, but here are a few ideas to keep you wondering ...

 *They help you work out which memories to keep from the day.*

2 *They help you learn how to deal with situations you've faced.*

3 *They are a way for your brain to organise information.*

4 *They prepare you for what you may face when you wake up.*

15

Write about your favourite dream here!

....

....

....

....

....

....

....

Profile: You!

You've joined the Winx Club! Fill in your fairy details, then design your fairy wings!

My Fairy Powers...

....

....

I LIKE: ....

I LOVE: ....

MY STRENGTHS: ....

MY FAVOURITE SPELL: ....

MY FAMILY: ....

....

MY HOME: ....

....

MY PIXIE FRIEND: ....

....

MY MAGIC PET: ....

....

Your Fairy Wings!

Fairy Friends Quiz

Which of Bloom's friends are you most like?

Start

What kind of party do you like best?

- 🦋 A slumber party with a few friends
- 🦋 One with loud music and lots of guests

Which kind of films do you like watching?

- 🦋 Ones with happy endings
- 🦋 Ones that are action-packed

Can you keep a secret?

- 🦋 Yes
- 🦋 I try to!

What kind of pet would you like?

- 🦋 A fluffy bunny
- 🦋 A lively puppy

In your group of friends are you ...

- 🦋 The quiet one
- 🦋 The funny one

What would you wear to a party?

- 🦋 A beautiful, flowing dress
- 🦋 Anything brightly coloured

Compared to your friends do you dress ...

- 🦋 To stand out
- 🦋 to blend in

When a friend is feeling sad, do you ...

- 🦋 Tell her a joke
- 🦋 Ask her what's wrong

Stella

You are most like Stella. You like the finer things in life and always like to look your best!

Stella's friendship tip:
Swap clothes with your friends to get a brand new look for free!

Aisha

Like Aisha, you are always on the move! You love dancing and playing sports and always wear colourful clothes.

Aisha's friendship tip:
Don't forget to tell your friends how great you think they are!

Flora

You are a child of nature like Flora. You love trees and flowers and caring for animals.

Flora's friendship tip:
Be there for your friends in both good times and bad.

19

Trix Trouble

The Trix have stolen Bloom's powers! What will they use them for?

The Winx are determined to help Bloom get her powers back. Meanwhile, the Trix use them to take over the witch school, Cloudtower. They put their headmistress, Miss Griffin, in the dungeon and imprison the Specialist wizard Riven there too.

"We're in charge now!" Icy boasts to them. "We'll begin with destroying Redfountain, then we'll capture the whole of Magix World!"

The Trix conjure up Creatures of the Dark to attack Professor Saladin and his pupils at the Redfountain wizard school. Bloom knows she must go to Cloudtower and take back her Dragon Powers!

As Sky, Bloom, Brandon and Stella go through the tunnels to Cloudtower, they are attacked by evil creatures. But they're saved by Riven, who has escaped from the dungeon. He apologises for working with the Trix. The Specialists are very glad to have him back! Miss Griffin also escapes, and she helps fight the Trix. Then she opens an escape portal to Alfea.

As everyone escapes, Bloom and Sky distract the evil creatures by flying at them on Sky's windrider. When the portal closes, Bloom and Sky fly off to Alfea, but when

Bloom hears Daphne calling her, she goes to Lake Roccaluce to see her.

Bloom enters the lake and sees Daphne in a magical vision. She tells Bloom not to worry about her past, it's her friends and family who make her who she is. Then Daphne shows her the crown of Domino and tells her, "You are a Princess, Bloom. Nobody can steal your past, your dreams or your powers. Look inside yourself and you will find them all," she smiles, as she disappears forever.

Bloom bursts out of the lake in fairy form shouting, "Magix Winx! Charmix!" as her Dragon form appears. She flies to Alfea to stop the Trix once and for all!

"Hold your positions!" shouts Miss Faragonda, as the Trix lead an army of Darkness to Alfea. The Winx use their Charmix powers to battle everything the Trix sends at them. But then Stormy's tornado spell backfires, and she and Darcy are captured.

Bloom and Icy race across the sky as they battle each other. They end up fighting over Lake Roccaluce.

"Is that the best you've got *witchy-poo*?" Bloom teases, as she avoids one of Icy's ice bolts.

"Aargh!" Icy screams furiously, as she throws an ice blast which hurls Bloom into the lake. Icy freezes it solid, but Bloom uses her powers to burst through the ice and defeat Icy. She then carries the unconscious Icy back to Alfea. Bloom then uses her Dragon Flame powers to blast away the remaining Dark Creatures, leaving peace and calm.

"Alright!" yell the Specialists, as the Winx hug Bloom and Sky pulls her into his arms for a kiss. Flora smiles at Mirta, the former pumpkin, who she has changed back into a witch!

Then it's time for the Trix to face their punishment. "They will be confined to Light Rock Monastery until we see fit to release them," Miss Griffin announces, as she leads them into a dimensional portal.

That night, the Winx fairies and the Specialist wizards have a party to end all parties at Alfea!

"I wonder what will happen next?" Bloom says to Sky.

"I don't know," he replies. "But we'll find out together," he smiles, as a shooting star darts across the sky towards the moon.

The End

Colourful Bloom

Bloom has a new power! Colour her in, then add her new power in the box below!

Bloom's new power:

....

....

....

Bloom's Fruit Crunch

Follow these easy steps to make Bloom's tasty fruit pudding!

For 2-4 friends you need:

1 box of strawberries
1 box of blackberries
A sieve
A spoon
1 glass per person
A packet of crunchy oat cereal
1 large pot of yoghurt

1

Put aside a couple of the strawberries and blackberries for decoration. Push the rest of the strawberries through the sieve to make a tasty fruit pulp. Then do the same with the blackberries.

2

Use a spoon to add the fruit, yoghurt and cereal into glasses in pretty layers as shown. Then decorate the top with the remaining whole fruits. Leave to chill in the fridge until you're ready to enjoy!

Other fruits work just as well!

Make one for each of your friends!

Profile:

Stella

26

All About Stella ...

FAIRY POWERS: Fairy of the Sun and Moon

LIKES: Makeovers and music

LOVES: Brandon and shopping

STRENGTHS: A great friend and awesome dresser!

FAVOURITE SPELL: Moon Ray

FAMILY: Stella's parents are the royal family of Solaria, King Radius and Queen Luna.

HOME: Solaria

PIXIE FRIEND: Amore, Pixie of Feelings. Like Stella, she loves matchmaking others!

MAGICAL PET: Ginger the Poodle

Draw some new shoes for Stella!

Follow the Fairies

Follow the fairies to find your way to the finish. You can go up, down, forwards or backwards, but not diagonally.

 Start

Follow this order

 Finish

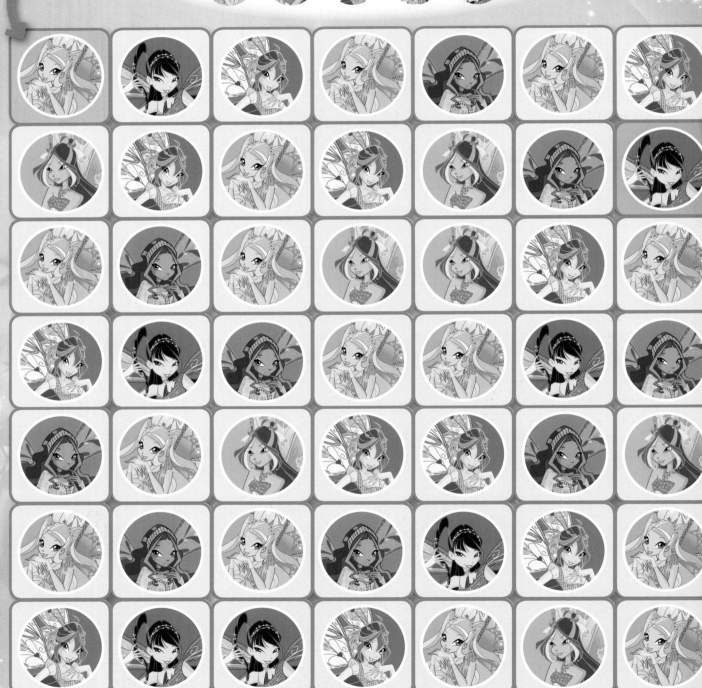

Friendship Necklace

Share this pretty necklace with your best friend!

You will need:
thin card
safety scissors
coloured felt
glue
ribbon
tape

optional:
sequins
beads

1

Cut out a heart shape from the card. Use that as a stencil to cut out the same heart shape from the felt. Glue the two together and leave to dry. Then cut the heart in half as shown in step 2.

2

Decorate both halves of the heart, perhaps with sequins and beads as shown. Then tape a loop of ribbon to the back of both hearts. The necklaces are now ready to share with your best friend!

29

Profile:
Aisha

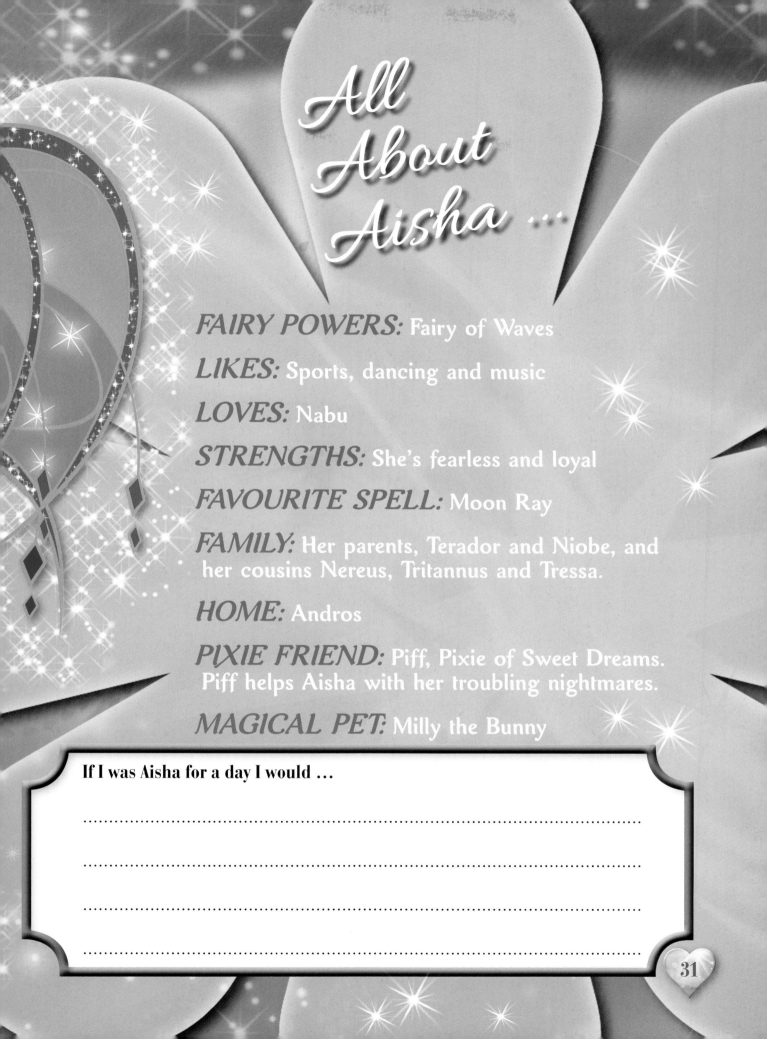

All About Aisha ...

FAIRY POWERS: Fairy of Waves

LIKES: Sports, dancing and music

LOVES: Nabu

STRENGTHS: She's fearless and loyal

FAVOURITE SPELL: Moon Ray

FAMILY: Her parents, Terador and Niobe, and her cousins Nereus, Tritannus and Tressa.

HOME: Andros

PIXIE FRIEND: Piff, Pixie of Sweet Dreams. Piff helps Aisha with her troubling nightmares.

MAGICAL PET: Milly the Bunny

If I was Aisha for a day I would …

....

....

....

....

Aisha and the Pixies

A fairy never gives up without a fight!

The Shadow Phoenix has kidnapped the Pixies! Can Aisha rescue them and stop his evil plans?

A young fairy called Aisha creeps into the Shadow Phoenix's Underground Castle to rescue the kidnapped Pixies. But the Phoenix sees her! As Aisha carries the Pixies across a bridge to escape, the Phoenix appears in front of her. He captures the Pixies in a glowing sphere and throws Aisha off a cliff! Bruised and battered, Aisha limps to Alfea, where she meets Bloom and Stella. They promise to help her rescue the Pixies from the Shadow Phoenix.

At Lightrock Monastery, the Trix smile evilly as they see the sky darken above them.

"Something wicked's in the air," smirks Icy, as the Phoenix appears.

"Come," he says to them, "I have need of your dark hearts."

The Phoenix conjures up Gloomix to give the Trix invincible evil powers.

"Now you serve *me*!" he tells them. "And soon so will the rest of the Magic Dimension, but first you must get the Codex for me from the Pixie Village!"

Stella, Bloom and Aisha go to the Phoenix's castle to free the Pixies. But as they draw near, the Trix attack them. Stella and Bloom transform with their Charmix powers, but they're soon overpowered. But then a stranger appears. He captures the Trix in a glowing sphere which disappears as he flies away.

Aisha introduces the Pixies to Stella and Bloom. Stella bonds with Amore, the Pixie of Feelings, and Bloom bonds with Lockette, the Pixie of Direction. The Phoenix watches from his throne room.

"My plan is working," he smirks. "Soon I will have the Pixie's secret *and* the Dragon Flame!"

The Winx cheer as Miss Faragonda allows Aisha and the Pixies to stay at Alfea. Then she introduces them to a new teacher, Professor Avalon.

"It's the winged man who rescued us at the Phoenix's castle," Stella gasps.

Professor Avalon tells Bloom that he can help her find out more about her past by hypnotising her. When he does, Bloom sees her birth family, but then a dark cloud appears which becomes a snarling monster. She doesn't remember much when she wakes up.

The next day, the Winx join the Specialists for the reopening of Redfountain. Sky notices that Bloom appears obsessed with Professor Avalon.

"It's like she's hypnotised," he says, as she follows him around.

That evening Professor Avalon hypnotises the Pixies into returning to their village. Icy follows and forces them to give her the Codex.

"At last!" says the Phoenix, when Icy gives it to him. "And now for the final part of my plan – Bloom and the Dragon Flame!"

Professor Avalon takes Bloom into a glowing sphere which transports them to the Phoenix's throne room. Avalon then reveals that he's the Shadow Phoenix!

"With you, the Fairy of the Dragon Flame, I will rule Magix!" he tells her.

The Phoenix hits Bloom with evil magic auras, which transforms her into Dark Bloom. She cackles as the Phoenix tells her to start the ritual to make him all-powerful. But the Trix quickly interrupt him.

"Aren't you forgetting *us*?" Icy asks him sharply.

"I send you back from where you came," the Phoenix chants, as the howling Trix are sucked back to a magic-free life at Lightrock Monastery.

The Phoenix uses the Codex to open the doorway to the Interplanetary Dimension. Bloom then begins the chant of power. The Pixies open the portal so the Winx and the Specialists can stop the Phoenix.

"The Doorway is opening and you are all doomed!" the Phoenix yells, as Bloom continues her dark chant.

"Bloom!" Sky pleads. "Fight for who you truly are! You are stronger than the Phoenix's evil powers and I care more about you than anyone else in the world."

As Bloom comes back to herself, she makes the evil magic disappear. The Specialists, Pixies and Winx join forces to fight the Phoenix.

"Charmix convergence!" shout the Winx, as their power for good defeats the Phoenix's evil plan. The Winx and their friends have saved the day once again!

The End

Style Queen Quiz

What's your party style?
Take the quiz to find out!

Start

Do you always know what you'll wear the next day, before going to bed?

of course!

erm, no

Would you lend your new outfit to your sister?

probably ...

not always

customise

When you get bored of your clothes do you give them away or customise them?

Do you try to make your school uniform look a little different?

give away

no

never

no

Do you have more trainers than pretty shoes?

yes

Your best skirt has a stain on it but it's not very noticeable. Do you still wear it?

yes

Someone's turned up in the same outfit as you. Do you think it's ...

a disaster!

funny!

Your new shoes hurt your feet but go with your outfit. What do you do?

wear them!

swap them

You've worn jeans to a party where everyone else is in dresses. Do you change?

definitely

no

Fashion Focussed

Like Stella, you have your finger on the style pulse. You spend time choosing your outfits and love to look perfect!

Smooth Stylist

You have fun with fashion, like Bloom. If you spilt something on your top, it wouldn't be the end of the world!

Chilled About Clothes

Like Tecna, you don't spend much time thinking about style. If your clothes are comfortable then all's good with you!

Profile: Flora

All About Flora ...

FAIRY POWERS: Fairy of Nature

LIKES: Flowers and trees

LOVES: Helia

STRENGTHS: She's caring, kind and nurturing

FAVOURITE SPELL: Giant Nettles

FAMILY: Her sister Miele.

HOME: Linphea

PIXIE FRIEND: Chatta, the Pixie of Gossip. She helps shy Flora to express herself.

MAGICAL PET: Coco the Cat

Flora has discovered a new kind of flower! What do you think it looks like? Draw it here.

Magic Flowers Maze

Powerful magic flowers have grown in the Magic Dimension. Help Flora find them all and deliver them to Alfea.

Start

Finish

41

Answer on page 69.

Disaster in Gardenia

The Winx have gained the power of Believix! They soon need all their powers to stop a disaster in Gardenia ...

The Winx are visiting Gardenia to bring magic to Earth. As the Specialists go to meet them at the Frutti Music beach bar, Prince Sky shows the wizards his Pendant of Eraklyon.

"I'm giving it to Bloom," he tells them. "When a ruler of Eraklyon presents it to his true love, they have good luck and happiness together for the rest of their lives."

"I'm sorry I had to spend so much of the summer at Eraklyon," Sky tells Bloom later.

"It's OK, you are Crown Prince after all," Bloom smiles at him. Sky is about to give Bloom the pendant when disaster strikes! Kiko leaps onto the table to get to a glass of carrot juice, but slips and knocks it at Sky. Sky gasps as the pendant falls out of the box. He grabs it just before it smashes on the ground. He puts it in his pocket to give to Bloom later.

Aisha calls her cousin Tressa using her camera phone. Tressa is the daughter of King Neptune and Queen Ligea and tonight Neptune is crowning either her brother Nereus or his twin, Tritannus, as his successor.

"Nereus is a real sweetie but Tritannus is a bit of a psycho," Aisha tells the Winx, as they crowd around her phone to watch the ceremony. But, when King Neptune makes his way to his throne, Tritannus is nowhere to be found, so Nereus is crowned as his successor.

But as Neptune goes to put a crown on his head, it is blasted out of his hands. Everyone panics and

Tressa's phone is knocked out of her hands, so Aisha's mobile screen goes blank!

At the coronation, Tritannus, wearing a mask, hits Nereus with an energy blast.

"Assassin!" shouts Neptune and fights him. As he pins him on the ground, he cuts off his mask, revealing Tritannus.

"You picked my brother. For this I will destroy you all!" Tritannus yells, as he's led to Andros Prison.

As Aisha calls Tressa, they hear a loud *BOOM*. An oil rig is on fire! Tecna scans it. "There are multiple pipeline ruptures and oil is flowing into the sea," she says.

"We've got to rescue the workers and stop the spill," replies Bloom, as the Winx and the Specialists rush to the rig.

Stella protects the workers from the fire and Musa's Harmonic Attack blasts a falling crane into the sea. Bloom's Fire Catcher absorbs the fire and Tecna's Tecnoshock removes the oil from the water. Flora then uses magic vines to fix the broken pipes, but oil is still leaking out from under the rig!

"Underwater Breath!" shouts Aisha, as she dives down to it. Above her, Sky helps the Foreman off a burning deck. But as he pulls him onto his windrider, the pendant of Eraklyon falls out of his pocket into the sea.

"Nooooo!" Sky cries, as he loses his grip on the windrider and both he and the Foreman fall towards the water. Bloom catches Sky, but the Foreman falls underwater, where Aisha rescues him.

Together, the Winx fix the remaining leaks. "Purifying Wind!" say Tecna and Musa. "Crystal Water!" say Aisha and Bloom. "Green Burst!" cry Flora and Stella. "Convergence!" they shout together, as a shimmering light dissolves the spill and makes the rig an eco-friendly organic structure.

"We didn't get all the oil," Flora says sadly. "There's a slick moving across the ocean floor." Tecna does some quick calculations.

"The spill could pollute thousands of miles of ocean," she tells the Winx.

"But now magic is on earth and in the oceans," Bloom replies.

"So pollution and magic could mix? Sounds like trouble," says Stella thoughtfully.

Deep under the ocean far away in the Magix World, Tritannus is locked in a cell at Andros Prison. He soon meets his neighbours, the Trix, who have been sent there after more bad behaviour. Tritannus smiles evilly. He knows they can help him escape!

The story continues on

PAGE 52 ...

Face Facts!

Your face shape and features can say a lot about you. See what Flora's says about her!

Deep-set eyes shows she's creative and romantic.

Button nose shows she's open and caring.

Full lips show that she's sensitive.

Oval face, showing she's totally honest.

Add colour to complete Flora's outfit.

What Are You Like?

Here are some ideas about what your features might say about you!

Eyes: People with close-set eyes tend to be trustworthy. Big eyes shows imagination and small-eyed people are organised.

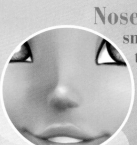

Nose: People with small noses tend to be kind. Active people often have long noses.

Lips: calm people often have thin lips. A fuller top lip shows a love of freedom. A fuller bottom lip shows generosity.

Face: round-faced people tend to look on the bright side. People with long faces can be really observant.

Draw your face here!

Body Language Top Tips:

1 If you fold your arms across your chest, people might think you're annoyed.

2 If you want to see if someone's really happy check out their eyes. They will sparkle if they're really happy, but if they don't mean it their smile won't go beyond their lips.

3 If someone copies your body language, it usually means they think you're great!

47

Profile:

Tecna

FAIRY POWERS:
Fairy of Technology

LIKES: Computers, mobile phones and all things digital!

LOVES: Timmy

STRENGTHS: She's rational and logical

FAVOURITE SPELL: Laser Ray

FAMILY: Unknown

HOME: Zenith

PIXIE FRIEND: Digit, the Pixie of Nanotechnology. Together, there's no technology that they can't master!

MAGICAL PET: Chicko the Duckling

Draw a new gadget that Tecna and the Winx can use to defeat the Trix!

Tecna's Secret Message

Help the Winx girls work out Tecna's message. Use the icons below to crack the code.

Super Sudoku

Draw in the missing pictures in this super Sudoku puzzle so ...

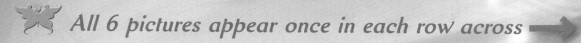 All 6 pictures appear once in each row across →

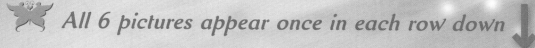 All 6 pictures appear once in each row down

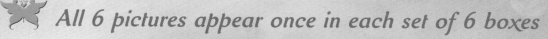 All 6 pictures appear once in each set of 6 boxes

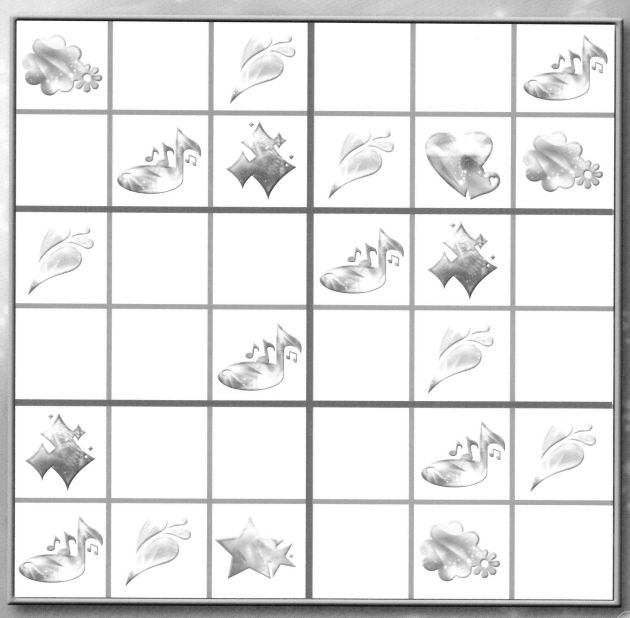

Answer on page 69.

Tritannus' Revenge

It's the night of the Winx benefit concert. Meanwhile the oil slick from Gardenia causes trouble in Andros ...

Everyone cheers as the Winx finish their final song of the benefit concert they've put on to raise money to clear up damage from the oil spill. As they leave the stage, Aisha's phone rings. It's Tressa, who tells her what happened at the coronation and how Tritannus is now in Andros prison.

Deep under the sea, the oil slick flows through the Earth Gate and heads for Andros. Philla and Lemmy, the keepers of the Ocean Gates of Earth and Andros, try to stop it, but it makes their powers fizzle out.

In Andros prison, Icy is chatting to Tritannus. "You *obviously* should be king," she tells him. But suddenly the oil from the spill flows over Tritannus. "It's toxic!" he cries, as his eyes go green and he transforms into a monster!

"I will make my father regret that he chose my brother over me!" Monster Tritannus growls, as he smashes his cell, freeing himself and the Trix.

Back at Gardenia beach, Sky tells Brandon that if the Crown Prince of Eraklyon loses the Eraklyon Pendant, like he has, it means he'll never be happy with the girl he loves. Sky is devastated. He thinks he can't be with Bloom.

Monster Tritannus blasts the prison guards with his trident, which turns them into mutants. He then uses his trident to suck the power out of Lemmy and Philla, so he can escape Andros.

"I'll rule the Magic Dimension!" he tells Icy.

"I just wish we could help," Icy

says sneakily. "If you could restore our powers ..."

Tritannus then transforms the witches into their evil selves again, but the effort is too much, and he turns back into his old self again.

"I think you ran out of toxic pollution," Icy tells him. "But we can get more on Earth!"

"Then that's where we'll go!" Tritannus replies.

In Gardenia, the Trix hypnotise some thugs into emptying toxic waste into the ocean, so they can turn Tritannus back into a monster. But then the Trix notice that there is magic in the air. They realise the Winx are in Gardenia too.

"Destroy the fairies!" Tritannus tells his mutants.

The people on Gardenia beach scream when they see the mutants coming out of the sea.

"Winx Transform! Believix!" yells Bloom, as they turn into fairies.

"Magic Echo!" shout Musa, taking down one of the mutants.

"Fire arrow!" calls Bloom, taking down the second mutant. Aisha gets hold of the third mutant's tail and swings it into the other two. Outnumbered, the mutants retreat back into the ocean.

Then Bloom is hit with an icy blast. "Haa-aay!" says Icy, giggling evilly at her.

"I thought you were in jail," Bloom replies.

"Things change!" Icy shouts, as she blasts Bloom again.

Together, Musa, Bloom and Stella use their magical powers to battle the Trix, while Aisha, Tecna and Flora follow the mutants down to the ocean floor. There, they see Monster Tritannus for the first time.

"You pathetic fairies think you can stop me? I will destroy you!" he shouts. But his powers are weakening and he flees back to the

Gate of Andros and uses his trident to swim through it. The Winx can't follow him.

"I can't believe that monster is my cousin," Aisha tells Flora and Tecna.

"We couldn't stop him. Our magic is too weak underwater," Flora adds.

The Winx realise they have to go back to Alfea and make their magic stronger so they can take on Tritannus and the Trix.

We'll find a way to fix everything," Bloom tells her parents. But no one sees Tritannus' face projected onto the water.

"Icy, I promise we will destroy those fairies ..." he cries.

"... together!" Icy cackles evilly in reply.

The Winx face troublesome times ahead with the joint evils of the Trix and Tritannus out to get them.

They'll need to work harder than ever to make good outshine evil!

The End

Profile:

Musa

All About Musa ...

FAIRY POWERS: Fairy of Music

LIKES: Singing and music

LOVES: Riven

STRENGTHS: She's always entertaining

FAVOURITE SPELL: Sonic Wave

FAMILY: Her dad, Ho-Boe

HOME: Melody

PIXIE FRIEND: Tune, the Pixie of Good Manners. Despite being complete opposites, Tune and Musa have a strong bond and learn from each other's strengths.

MAGIC PETS: Pepe the Bear

Colour in Musa's musical notes!

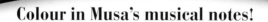

Musa's Singing Quiz

It's time to sing like Musa but what's your style? Take this fun quiz to find out!

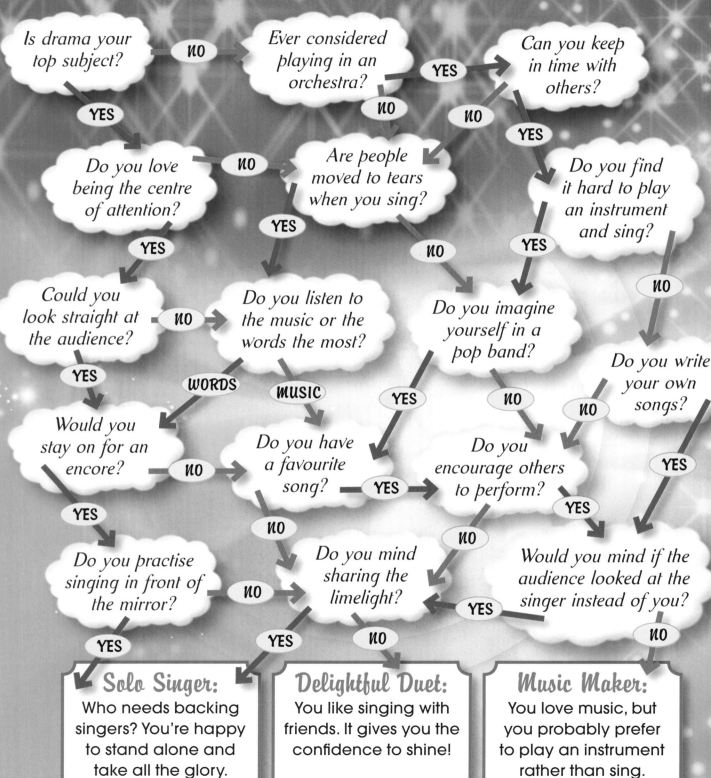

Is drama your top subject? — **NO** → **Ever considered playing in an orchestra?** — **YES** → **Can you keep in time with others?**

Is drama your top subject? — **YES** → **Do you love being the centre of attention?**

Ever considered playing in an orchestra? — **NO** → **Are people moved to tears when you sing?**

Can you keep in time with others? — **NO** → **Are people moved to tears when you sing?**

Can you keep in time with others? — **YES** → **Do you find it hard to play an instrument and sing?**

Do you love being the centre of attention? — **NO** → **Are people moved to tears when you sing?**

Do you love being the centre of attention? — **YES** → **Could you look straight at the audience?**

Are people moved to tears when you sing? — **YES** → **Do you listen to the music or the words the most?**

Are people moved to tears when you sing? — **NO** → **Do you imagine yourself in a pop band?**

Do you find it hard to play an instrument and sing? — **YES** → **Do you imagine yourself in a pop band?**

Do you find it hard to play an instrument and sing? — **NO** → **Do you write your own songs?**

Could you look straight at the audience? — **NO** → **Would you stay on for an encore?**

Could you look straight at the audience? — **YES** → **Would you stay on for an encore?**

Do you listen to the music or the words the most? — **WORDS** → **Would you stay on for an encore?**

Do you listen to the music or the words the most? — **MUSIC** → **Do you have a favourite song?**

Do you imagine yourself in a pop band? — **YES** → **Do you have a favourite song?**

Do you imagine yourself in a pop band? — **NO** → **Do you encourage others to perform?**

Do you write your own songs? — **NO** → **Do you encourage others to perform?**

Do you write your own songs? — **YES** → **Would you mind if the audience looked at the singer instead of you?**

Would you stay on for an encore? — **NO** → **Do you have a favourite song?**

Would you stay on for an encore? — **YES** → **Do you practise singing in front of the mirror?**

Do you have a favourite song? — **YES** → **Do you encourage others to perform?**

Do you have a favourite song? — **NO** → **Do you mind sharing the limelight?**

Do you encourage others to perform? — **NO** → **Do you mind sharing the limelight?**

Do you encourage others to perform? — **YES** → **Would you mind if the audience looked at the singer instead of you?**

Would you mind if the audience looked at the singer instead of you? — **YES** → **Do you mind sharing the limelight?**

Do you practise singing in front of the mirror? — **NO** → **Do you mind sharing the limelight?**

Do you practise singing in front of the mirror? — **YES** → **Solo Singer**

Do you mind sharing the limelight? — **YES** → **Solo Singer**

Do you mind sharing the limelight? — **NO** → **Delightful Duet**

Would you mind if the audience looked at the singer instead of you? — **NO** → **Music Maker**

Solo Singer:
Who needs backing singers? You're happy to stand alone and take all the glory.

Delightful Duet:
You like singing with friends. It gives you the confidence to shine!

Music Maker:
You love music, but you probably prefer to play an instrument rather than sing.

58

Musa's Party Maze

Help Musa find her way through
the maze to join her friends at the party.

Answer on page 69.

1

PARTY TIP:
A party's only
a party when
all your friends
are there.

2

PARTY TIP:
Make special food.
Remember what your
friends like, so you
know they'll enjoy
your treat!

3

PARTY TIP:
Games are a great way
to have fun as a group.
It could be board games,
computer games or take
turns to dance!

4

PARTY TIP:
Play your friends'
favourite tunes to
show how much you
like them.

59

Friendship Quiz

PLAYER 1 QUESTIONS

1 What's her favourite film? _____

What's your favourite film? _____

2 What's her favourite colour? _____

What's your favourite colour? _____

3 What's her biggest fear? _____

What's your biggest fear? _____

4 What's her dream pet? _____

What's your dream pet? _____

5 What's her favourite song? _____

What's your favourite song? _____

6 Who's her favourite Winx fairy? _____

Who's your favourite Winx fairy? _____

SCORE

WHAT'S YOUR SCORE?

Results:
- 1-2 Plan a sleepover to get to know each other better!
- 3-4 You're firm friends!
- 5-6 Well done, you're total best friends!

60

How to Play:

1. Sit opposite your best friend with the Annual lying between you.
2. Answer the questions and don't peek at each other's answers!
3. Give yourself a point for each one you get right.

SCORE

PLAYER 2 QUESTIONS

1 What's her favourite film? _____

What's your favourite film? _____

2 What's her favourite colour? _____

What's your favourite colour? _____

3 What's her biggest fear? _____

What's your biggest fear? _____

4 What's her dream pet? _____

What's your dream pet? _____

5 What's her favourite song? _____

What's your favourite song? _____

6 Who's her favourite Winx fairy? _____

Who's your favourite Winx fairy? _____

WHAT'S YOUR SCORE?

Results:
- 1-2 Plan a sleepover to get to know each other better!
- 3-4 You're firm friends!
- 5-6 Well done, you're total best friends!

61

Horoscopes 2014

What might 2014 bring for you and the Winx girls?
Read on to find out!

Aries
21 March – 20 April
You're going on a very special journey. It might be far away or just around the corner, but wherever it is, it's guaranteed to be fun!

Taurus
21 April – 21 May
Got exams coming up? This year you'll need to work really hard at your studies, but it will all be worth it in the end!

Gemini
22 May – 21 June
You've got so many plans in your head that it's hard to stick to just one! Make a list of everything you'd like to do this year to help you to make up your mind.

Cancer
22 June – 23 July
If you are feeling active, this year is the time to start flexing those sporty muscles and try something you've never done before!

Leo
24 July – 23 August
You and your best friend are going to have so much fun this year! If there's something you've always wanted to do together, now's the time!

Virgo
24 August – 23 Sept
Your stars are predicting a creative year for you! You could be the star of a school play or start writing a novel!

LIBRA
24 Sept – 23 Oct
Make a wish early in the year and by Christmas it might just come true. You've got luck in your stars this year!

SCORPIO
24 Oct – 22 Nov
This year is all about helping others. You may have an upset friend to deal with or a little brother or sister who needs your guidance.

SAGTTARIUS
23 Nov – 21 Dec
You're in for a makeover this year! If you're tired of the same old look, take your time and seek out the real you.

CAPRICORN
22 Dec – 20 Jan
It's all about the outdoors for you! And you don't have to go far to enjoy it. Ask your parents if you can have a vegetable patch in your back garden.

AQUARIUS
21 Jan – 19 Feb
The stars are thinking about your future, and so are you! This year, start to plan how to achieve your dreams.

PISCES
20 Feb – 20 March
You're going to meet a new friend this year who's going to be loads of fun. But make sure you don't forget your old mates!

Winx Bithdays!

Flora – 1st March

Musa – 30th May

Aisha – 15th June

Stella – 18th August

Bloom – 10th December

Tecna – 16th December

What birthday wishes do you want to come true this year?

....

....

....

....

....

Smoothie Surprise

Fruit smoothies are yummy treats to make for your friends.

For two people you need:
1 banana (peeled and chopped)
2 oranges (peeled)
10 strawberries (stalks removed)
or half a glass of frozen berries.
2 glasses
2 straws

What you do:

1 Pull the oranges into segments and put them in a large jug with the chopped banana.

2 Add the strawberries or frozen berries.

3 Whizz the fruit together using a hand-held mixer for 2–3 minutes until the mixture is thick and smooth.

4 Pour the mixture into two glasses. Then decorate with a strawberry or orange slice and enjoy!

Note to parents: Adult supervision is recommended when knives, electric equipment and glasses are being used.

64

Pattern Power

Use pattern power to complete these pretty patterns by adding the right shape in the box at the end of each row.

Answers on page 69.

See You Soon!

Add colour to complete this picture of the Winx fairies, then wave goodbye to them!

Reader Survey

Ask a grown-up to help you fill in this form and post it to the address at the end by 28th February 2014, or you can fill in the survey online at www.egmont.co.uk/winxsurvey2014

One lucky reader will win £150 of book tokens! Five runners-up will win a £25 book token each.

1. Who bought this Winx Annual?

- ♡ Me
- ♡ Parent/guardian
- ♡ Grandparent
- ♡ Other (please specify)

_____

2. Why did they buy it?

- ♡ Christmas present
- ♡ Birthday present
- ♡ I'm a collector
- ♡ Other (please specify)

_____

3. What are your favourite parts of the Winx Annual?

Stories	♡ Really like	♡ Like	♡ Don't like
Puzzles	♡ Really like	♡ Like	♡ Don't like
Quizzes	♡ Really like	♡ Like	♡ Don't like
Colouring	♡ Really like	♡ Like	♡ Don't like
Character Profiles	♡ Really like	♡ Like	♡ Don't like
Things to Make	♡ Really like	♡ Like	♡ Don't like

4. Do you think the stories are too long, too short or about right?

- ♡ Too long
- ♡ Too short
- ♡ About right

5. Do you think the activities are too hard, too easy or about right?

- ♡ Too hard
- ♡ Too easy
- ♡ About right

6. Apart from Bloom, who are your favourite characters?

(1) _____

(2) _____

(3) _____

7. Which other annuals do you like?

(1) _____

(2) _____

(3) _____

8. What is your favourite ...

(1) ... app or website?

_____

(2) ... console game?

_____

(3) ... magazine?

_____

(4) ... book?

_____

9. What are your favourite TV programmes?

(1) _____

(2) _____

(3) _____

10. Would you like to get the Winx Annual again next year?

♡ Yes   ♡ No

Why? _____

_____

_____

Thank you!

(Please ask your parent/guardian to complete)

Child's name: _____ Age: _____ Boy / Girl

Parent/guardian name: _____

Parent/guardian signature: _____

Parent/guardian email address: _____

Daytime telephone number: _____

♡ Please send me the Egmont Monthly Catch-Up Newsletter.

Please cut out and post to:
Winx Annual Reader Survey
Egmont UK Limited
The Yellow Building
1 Nicholas Road
London W11 4AN

Good luck!

Answers

Magic Flowers Maze
Page 40

Super Sudoku
Page 51

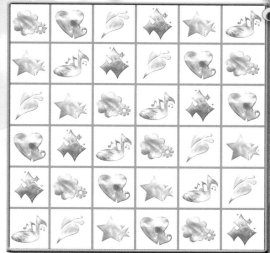

Pattern Power
Page 65

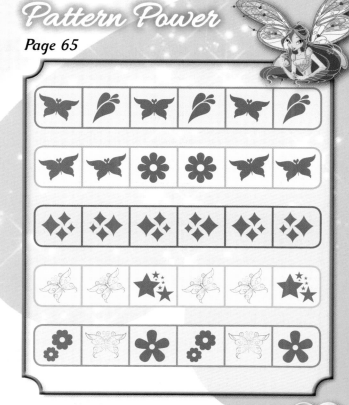

Musa's Party Maze
Page 59